D1094703

JOSEPH
and His Brothers

By Maud and Miska Petersham

An American ABC
America's Stamps
A Bird in the Hand
The Box with Red Wheels
The Boy Who Had No Heart
The Circus Baby
David
Jesus' Story
Joseph
Moses
My Very First Book
Off to Bed
The Rooster Crows
Ruth
The Silver Mace
The Story of Jesus
Story of the Presidents

JOSEPH and His Brothers

FROM THE STORY TOLD IN THE BOOK OF GENESIS

MAUD and MISKA PETERSHAM

THE MACMILLAN COMPANY • NEW YORK • 1958

CONTENTS

THE COAT OF MANY COLORS

JOSEPH IN THE LAND OF EGYPT

THE BROTHERS GO TO EGYPT

JACOB AND HIS SONS

Jacob and his sons dwelt in the land of Canaan,
which was the land of Abraham and of Isaac.

THE COAT OF MANY COLORS

THERE was a boy named Joseph, who had many brothers. He had ten brothers who were much older and one younger brother, Benjamin.

The father, Jacob, owned flocks of sheep and goats and great herds of cattle. And the sons helped to care for their father's flocks. Jacob and his family lived in tents on the hillsides of the land of Canaan.

Joseph's mother was dead, but his father, Jacob, loved him dearly, even more than he loved his other sons. As a mark of his favor, he gave Joseph a coat of many colors.

The brothers were jealous of Joseph, and when he told them of a dream he had, they hated him still more. For Joseph had dreamed that he was working in the field with his brothers, when suddenly the bundle of wheat that he was binding stood upright, and each of the brothers' bundles bowed down before it.

Joseph dreamed yet another dream in which the sun, the moon, and the eleven stars bowed down to him. This dream made the brothers still more angry.

Soon after this, the elder brothers went far away from home with the flocks to find richer fields. Time passed and Jacob, the father, wanted to know if all was well with his sons and with the flocks.

So Jacob sent the boy Joseph to find his brothers and to bring word back to him. Joseph went through the valleys and over the hills and at last he found his brothers.

When they saw him coming from far off, even before he came near to them, they said to

one another, "Behold, this dreamer cometh. Come now therefore, and let us slay him, and cast him into some pit. And we will say, 'Some evil beast hath devoured him.'"

But the eldest brother, Reuben, persuaded the others that it would be better not to kill Joseph, but rather to leave him in a pit there in the wilderness. Reuben thought to himself that when the others had gone, he could go back and draw his brother Joseph out of the pit and take him to his father.

When Joseph came up to his brothers, they did as they planned. They stripped Joseph out of his coat of many colors and cast him into a pit. The pit was empty. There was not even water in it.

The brothers themselves sat down to eat. While they were eating, they saw a company of men and camels coming over the hills. It was a caravan on its way to Egypt, carrying spices, balm, and myrrh.

Then Judah, another of Joseph's brothers, said to the rest, "Let us not leave Joseph to die in the pit. Let us sell him to these merchants."

So they drew him up out of the pit and sold him to the merchants for twenty pieces of silver. And the caravan went on its way to Egypt, carrying Joseph with it.

The brothers took Joseph's coat of many colors. They killed a goat and dipped the coat in its blood. Then they returned to their father and gave him the coat, saying that they had found it.

When Jacob saw his son's coat, he believed
that Joseph was dead, and he mourned and
wept for his son and refused to be comforted.

JOSEPH IN THE LAND OF EGYPT

WHEN the merchants came to Egypt, they sold Joseph to an Egyptian named Potiphar who was captain of the guard under Pharaoh, the king. God was with Joseph, and the lad served Potiphar well and in time was given charge over all his household.

At first all went well; then his master blamed Joseph for something he had not done. He took him and put him into the prison where the king's prisoners were kept.

While Joseph was in prison, Pharaoh, the king, became angry with the chief of his butlers and the chief of his bakers, and they were also put into the prison.

In the dungeon the butler and the baker each had a strange dream, and Joseph was able to explain the meaning of their dreams. He told the baker that within three days he would die but that the butler would be taken back by the king.

It happened just as Joseph had said. In three days' time the baker was hanged and the butler was returned to his place with Pharaoh. But the butler forgot Joseph. Two years passed, and Joseph was still in prison.

Then it happened that Pharaoh, the king, dreamed and was troubled. He called all the magicians of Egypt and all the wise men to him, but not one of them could tell Pharaoh the meaning of his dreams.

Pharaoh took his ring from his hand and put it upon Joseph's hand. He gave him the finest linen clothing and put a chain of gold about his neck and gave him the second of his chariots in which to ride. And Joseph went throughout all the land.

It happened just as Joseph had said. There came seven years of great plenty in Egypt. During those good years, Joseph commanded the people in the cities to store up the food of the fields. Joseph gathered grain like the sands of

the sea, so much that he could not keep account of it.

The seven years of plenty ended. And then began the seven years of want. There was famine in all lands. The people cried to Pharaoh for bread. Pharaoh sent them to Joseph to do whatever he said. Joseph opened the storehouses and sold the grain to the Egyptians. Men from all countries came into Egypt to buy grain, because the famine was so great in all lands.

THE BROTHERS GO TO EGYPT

THE famine was great even in the land of Canaan. And when Jacob saw that the Egyptians had grain, he told his sons to go down into Egypt and buy food so that they might live and not die. The ten brothers went, but the father would not let Benjamin go with them for he feared that something evil might happen to him.

So when the brothers reached Egypt, they came before Joseph and bowed down with their faces to the earth.

Joseph knew his brothers but they did not know him. He made himself strange to them and asked who they were. They told him that they were twelve brothers, sons of Jacob, in the land of Canaan. They told him that one brother was dead and that the youngest was at home with their father.

Joseph accused them of being spies and put them in prison for three days.

Then Joseph told them to return home with grain for their families and to bring the youngest brother back to him that he might know they were speaking truthfully. But he kept Simeon as a prisoner until the others returned.

Joseph had the sacks filled with grain. He had the money which each brother had given

for the grain put into the top of each sack. He gave them food for the journey, and they loaded the sacks on their donkeys and departed.

On the way one of the brothers opened his sack to get food for his donkey and he found the money. And when the brothers saw the money, they were troubled.

They came to the land of Canaan to Jacob, their father, and told him all that had happened. They told him how they had left their brother Simeon with Joseph in Egypt and how the ruler of Egypt had said they must bring their youngest brother to him.

Jacob was grieved and he said to them, "Joseph is not, and Simeon is not, and now ye will take Benjamin away." And he would not let him go.

But the famine was great in the land, and when they had eaten up all the grain which they had brought from Egypt, their father said, "Go again and buy us a little food."

The sons did not dare go without their brother Benjamin. At last their father said that if it must be so, then he would let Benjamin go.

He told them to take a present to this ruler of Egypt, the best fruits of the land, a little balm, a little honey, spices and myrrh, nuts and almonds. He also told them to take twice as much money, as well as the money they had found in their sacks, and to take Benjamin, their brother with them.

Again the brothers came into Egypt and stood before Joseph. When Joseph saw that Benjamin was with them, he told his steward to prepare a feast and to invite the brothers to dine with him at noon. The brothers were taken to Joseph's house, and Simeon was brought from the prison. But the brothers were very much afraid.

When Joseph came, they gave him the presents and bowed themselves to the earth before him. Joseph talked with them and asked them if their father were still alive and well.

When he lifted his eyes and looked at his young brother Benjamin, he could not help weeping. And he went into his own room and wept there.

Then he washed his face and came back and
the feast began. He sat by himself, for the
Hebrews were not allowed to eat at the same
table wth the Egyptians. The brothers were
seated in order of age from the eldest down to

the youngest. And they wondered that Joseph knew their ages.

From the food before him, Joseph sent a part to the brothers. To Benjamin he gave five times as much as he gave to the others. Then they feasted and drank together.

Joseph ordered his steward to fill the brothers' sacks with grain and again to put every man's money in the top of his sack. But in the top of Benjamin's sack Joseph had the

servant put his own silver cup as well as the
money.

In the morning as soon as it was light, the
brothers started home. When they had gone
but a little way out of the city, Joseph's steward
caught up with them and told them that the
silver cup of his master had been stolen. The
brothers knew they had not taken the cup. But
each man quickly took down his sack from the
donkey's back and opened it.

The steward looked in each sack. He began at the sack of the eldest and went to the youngest. And when he came to the lad Benjamin's sack, he found the silver cup.

In grief the brothers rent their clothes and returned to the city. They came to Joseph's house and fell before him on the ground. Joseph said that Benjamin, the brother in whose sack the cup had been found, must stay with him.

Judah, one of the elder brothers, came near to Joseph and begged him to let Benjamin go. He said that their father would die if Benjamin did not return. He begged that he himself might stay as a slave if only Benjamin could go back to his father.

Then Joseph could not refrain himself before all them that stood by him. So he sent away every man except the brothers.

When he was alone with his brothers, he made himself known to them and said, "I am Joseph." He wept aloud, and the Egyptians and the house of Pharaoh heard.

The brothers were troubled, and they did

not understand. Again he said, "I am Joseph, your brother, whom ye sold into Egypt."

He told them not to be angry with themselves because they had done this thing, for now he was a ruler in Egypt and would be able to save his family. Only two years of the famine were over, and there would be five more years in which there would be no harvest. He told his brothers to go quickly to his father and bring him down also into Egypt where there was plenty.

And he fell upon his brother Benjamin's neck and wept, and Benjamin wept. Then Joseph kissed all his brothers and talked with them.

JACOB AND HIS SONS

THE brothers hastened back with food and wagons from Egypt. Then they brought their father, Jacob, and their wives and little ones to dwell near Joseph in the land of Egypt.

Joseph made ready his chariot and went to meet his father. When Jacob saw his son Joseph, he was filled with joy and said, "Now

let me die, since I have seen thy face, because thou art yet alive."

Jacob and his sons and their families dwelt in the land of Egypt, and many children were born to them there.

Jacob was also called Israel, and before he died, he called his twelve sons to him and blessed them.

Each of the twelve sons of Jacob became the father of a tribe of people. These people were the Hebrews and were called the Children of Israel. For four hundred years they lived in the land of Egypt and they grew and prospered, and the land was filled with them.